National Gallery *of* Ireland
Gailearaí Náisiúnta *na* hÉireann

DIARY 2017

National Gallery *of* IRELAND

Michael Healy, *Saint Victor of Amiens,* **1930**

This sketch was made for a window in St Catherine's and St James's Church, Donore Avenue, Dublin 8. When Healy received this commission in 1930, the church was known as St Victor's. This preparatory pencil and watercolour design was sent to the Archbishop of Dublin, who sanctioned it in May 1930. The composition shows St Victor as a Roman soldier surrounded by a border of vignettes. The composition of the final window, completed by November 1930, closely resembles this sketch, though the colours in the stained glass are stronger, dominated by rich purples, reds and blues.

FRONT COVER William John Leech, *A Convent Garden, Brittany,* **c.1913**

Leech convalesced from typhoid in Concarneau, in a hospital run by the Sisters of the Holy Ghost, whose garden was the setting for this luminous picture. The model for the novice is Elizabeth Saurine, the artist's first wife. She glides past the viewer attired in a white lace habit, symbolic of her becoming a bride of Christ. Its delicate shades reflect the colours of the leaves and petals of the lilies, a symbol of purity.

TITLE PAGE Samuel Lover, *Portrait of Eliza O'Neill, (1791–1872), Actress, as Juliet,* **c.1830s**

O'Neill was born in Drogheda, County Louth, and began acting as a child. She made her London début as Juliet in Covent Garden in 1814. This idealised portrait of Eliza in the role of Juliet, wearing medieval costume, probably dates from much later. Her success was immediate and she was soon in demand for the major tragic roles. O'Neill was admired for her classic beauty, Grecian profile, voice and carriage, and was celebrated as successor to Sarah Siddons as a tragedienne. Her career ended in 1830 when she married Sir William Wrixon-Becher, MP for Mallow.

BACK COVER Roderic O'Conor, *Pink Sky, Cassis/La Rose du Ciel, Cassis,* **1913**

In 1913, O'Conor rented Villa Marguerite at Cassis near Marseilles in the south of France. The house was on a narrow street in the old town, on a hill leading up from the port, and afforded views across the valley to the bay of Cassis. O'Conor's sojourn there presented an opportunity for a new departure in his work. The dry terrain bathed in hot sunshine, the intense colours and tonal contrasts of the landscape are all reflected in the luminous tones of this work, which reveals the influence of Pierre Bonnard.

ENDPAPERS Unknown, *Dublin,* **late 18th/early 19th century**

Ink and watercolour on paper drawing of Dublin.

Keep in touch with the National Gallery of Ireland:

www.nationalgallery.ie

Twitter @NGI Ireland

Facebook.com/nationalgalleryofireland

Gill Books
Hume Avenue, Park West, Dublin 12
www.gillbooks.ie

Gill Books is an imprint of M.H. Gill & Co.

© The National Gallery of Ireland 2016/2017
978 0 7171 7222 1

Text researched and written by Sara Donaldson
Design by Tony Potter
Photography by Roy Hewson and Chris O'Toole/NGI

Print origination by Teapot Press Ltd
Printed in the EU

This book is typeset in Dax.

The paper used in this book comes from the wood pulp of managed forests. For every tree felled, at least one tree is planted, thereby renewing natural resources.

A CIP catalogue record for this book is available from the British Library.

5 4 3 2 1

2017

January • Eanáir
M T W T F S S
26 27 28 29 30 31 1
2 3 4 5 6 7 8
9 10 11 12 13 14 15
16 17 18 19 20 21 22
23 24 25 26 27 28 29
30 31 1 2 3 4 5

February • Feabhra
M T W T F S S
30 31 1 2 3 4 5
6 7 8 9 10 11 12
13 14 15 16 17 18 19
20 21 22 23 24 25 26
27 28 1 2 3 4 5

March • Márta
M T W T F S S
27 28 1 2 3 4 5
6 7 8 9 10 11 12
13 14 15 16 17 18 19
20 21 22 23 24 25 26
27 28 29 30 31 1 2

April • Aibreán
M T W T F S S
27 28 29 30 31 1 2
3 4 5 6 7 8 9
10 11 12 13 14 15 16
17 18 19 20 21 22 23
24 25 26 27 28 29 30

May • Bealtaine
M T W T F S S
1 2 3 4 5 6 7
8 9 10 11 12 13 14
15 16 17 18 19 20 21
22 23 24 25 26 27 28
29 30 31 1 2 3 4

June • Meitheamh
M T W T F S S
29 30 31 1 2 3 4
5 6 7 8 9 10 11
12 13 14 15 16 17 18
19 20 21 22 23 24 25
26 27 28 29 30 1 2

July • Iúil
M T W T F S S
26 27 28 29 30 1 2
3 4 5 6 7 8 9
10 11 12 13 14 15 16
17 18 19 20 21 22 23
24 25 26 27 28 29 30
31 1 2 3 4 5 6

August • Lúnasa
M T W T F S S
31 1 2 3 4 5 6
7 8 9 10 11 12 13
14 15 16 17 18 19 20
21 22 23 24 25 26 27
28 29 30 31 1 2 3

September • Meán Fómhair
M T W T F S S
28 29 30 31 1 2 3
4 5 6 7 8 9 10
11 12 13 14 15 16 17
18 19 20 21 22 23 24
25 26 27 28 29 30 1

October • Deireadh Fómhair
M T W T F S S
25 26 27 28 29 30 1
2 3 4 5 6 7 8
9 10 11 12 13 14 15
16 17 18 19 20 21 22
23 24 25 26 27 28 29
30 31 1 2 3 4 5

November • Samhain
M T W T F S S
30 31 1 2 3 4 5
6 7 8 9 10 11 12
13 14 15 16 17 18 19
20 21 22 23 24 25 26
27 28 29 30 1 2 3

December • Nollaig
M T W T F S S
27 28 29 30 1 2 3
4 5 6 7 8 9 10
11 12 13 14 15 16 17
18 19 20 21 22 23 24
25 26 27 28 29 30 31

2018

January • Eanáir
M T W T F S S
1 2 3 4 5 6 7
8 9 10 11 12 13 14
15 16 17 18 19 20 21
22 23 24 25 26 27 28
29 30 31 1 2 3 4

February • Feabhra
M T W T F S S
29 30 31 1 2 3 4
5 6 7 8 9 10 11
12 13 14 15 16 17 18
19 20 21 22 23 24 25
26 27 28 1 2 3 4

March • Márta
M T W T F S S
26 27 28 1 2 3 4
5 6 7 8 9 10 11
12 13 14 15 16 17 18
19 20 21 22 23 24 25
26 27 28 29 30 31 1

April • Aibreán
M T W T F S S
26 27 28 29 30 31 1
2 3 4 5 6 7 8
9 10 11 12 13 14 15
16 17 18 19 20 21 22
23 24 25 26 27 28 29
30 1 2 3 4 5 6

May • Bealtaine
M T W T F S S
30 1 2 3 4 5 6
7 8 9 10 11 12 13
14 15 16 17 18 19 20
21 22 23 24 25 26 27
28 29 30 31 1 2 3

June • Meitheamh
M T W T F S S
28 29 30 31 1 2 3
4 5 6 7 8 9 10
11 12 13 14 15 16 17
18 19 20 21 22 23 24
25 26 27 28 29 30 1

July • Iúil
M T W T F S S
25 26 27 28 29 30 1
2 3 4 5 6 7 8
9 10 11 12 13 14 15
16 17 18 19 20 21 22
23 24 25 26 27 28 29
30 31 1 2 3 4 5

August • Lúnasa
M T W T F S S
30 31 1 2 3 4 5
6 7 8 9 10 11 12
13 14 15 16 17 18 19
20 21 22 23 24 25 26
27 28 29 30 31 1 2

September • Meán Fómhair
M T W T F S S
27 28 29 30 31 1 2
3 4 5 6 7 8 9
10 11 12 13 14 15 16
17 18 19 20 21 22 23
24 25 26 27 28 29 30

October • Deireadh Fómhair
M T W T F S S
1 2 3 4 5 6 7
8 9 10 11 12 13 14
15 16 17 18 19 20 21
22 23 24 25 26 27 28
29 30 31 1 2 3 4

November • Samhain
M T W T F S S
29 30 31 1 2 3 4
5 6 7 8 9 10 11
12 13 14 15 16 17 18
19 20 21 22 23 24 25
26 27 28 29 30 1 2

December • Nollaig
M T W T F S S
26 27 28 29 30 1 2
3 4 5 6 7 8 9
10 11 12 13 14 15 16
17 18 19 20 21 22 23
24 25 26 27 28 29 30
31 1 2 3 4 5 6

The National Gallery of Ireland Diary for 2017 draws on the riches of the National Gallery's collection. It includes over fifty works in different media, depicting people, still lifes, landscapes and genre scenes. Some, such as the works on paper included, are held in the Prints & Drawings collection and are rarely on public display, to preserve them for posterity, making their inclusion among these pages very welcome. Other works, such as oil paintings by Thomas Gainsborough, Rembrandt van Rijn and Diego Velázquez de Silva, are acknowledged masterpieces of the Gallery's collection and are almost always on public display. Examples from the Irish collection are included, such as paintings by William Orpen and John Lavery, and new acquisitions, namely *The Resurrection of Christ* by the Flemish painter Maerten de Vos and a powerfully rendered etching by Roderic O'Conor, are featured for the first time.

Many of the paintings in this year's Diary are back on display following the opening of the refurbished Dargan and Milltown Wings. A hugely positive development, it has been well worth the wait. The Gallery's extended building phase has spectacularly transformed those wings. Behind the scenes and invisible to visitors, air handling and fire suppression technologies have been threaded through the existing structures. Using underground ducts and existing voids throughout the building, a new energy centre sited under the front lawn introduces the latest international standards of collection care in these sections of the Gallery for the first time. Visible to all are the beautifully restored and much-loved galleries of the Dargan and Milltown Wings.

Other significant changes include the opening of windows previously bricked up. Windows along one side of the Shaw Room and along one suite of galleries in the Milltown Wing now open onto a newly created and breath-taking courtyard. This visually links different levels of the Gallery and dramatically simplifies the process for visitors navigating between those spaces. Indeed, light from re-exposed windows, re-glazed roofs and stunning new light-boxes in the Milltown Wing humanises the entire experience of being in and moving through these spaces, much enhancing the quality of visits to the Gallery.

The refurbishment phases of the Gallery's Master Development Plan also set a standard for the final phase, yet to be started but already planned in detail. Ambition to complete the MDP will occupy the Gallery in the coming period. The final phase increases still further the ease with which visitors will circulate through the Gallery, providing public access to the education, library and archive facilities at the heart of the institution, as well as a purpose-built conservation block to assist in the care of the Gallery's collection, one of our core tasks. The Gallery will use the positive momentum generated by the reopening in 2017 to advance the case with the government and the Gallery's supporters for completing the Master Development Plan in its entirety.

Meanwhile, the availability of the fine spaces in the Dargan and Milltown Wings has allowed the curatorial staff to reimagine the permanent displays. Within a broadly chronological display, the Irish collections are prominent at ground level with European art on the first floor. The grand scale of the Shaw Room and monumental galleries upstairs give the displays a renewed sense of space and grandeur. The Gallery now breathes again as a place to explore and enjoy for all our visitors and supporters.

Sean Rainbird, Director of the National Gallery of Ireland

George Russell (AE), *Portrait of Iseult Gonne (Mrs Francis Stuart),* **20th century**

Iseult Gonne (1894–1954), the daughter of Maud Gonne, was, like her famous mother, considered a great beauty and she attracted the admiration of literary figures including Lennox Robinson, Ezra Pound and W.B. Yeats. Iseult married the Irish poet and novelist Francis Stuart, whom she first met at George Russell's home in 1918. Russell depicts her as an attractive brown-eyed young woman, wearing her hair in a loose bun and dressed in a patterned blue blouse which is echoed by the deeper blue curtain behind her.

26 Monday · Luan

27 Tuesday · Máirt

28 Wednesday · Céadaoin

29 Thursday · Déardaoin

30 Friday · Aoine

31 Saturday · Satharn
New Year's Eve

1 Sunday · Domhnach
New Year's Day

2017 January · Eanáir

Diego Velázquez de Silva, *Kitchen Maid with the Supper at Emmaus,* **c.1617–1618**

The *Supper at Emmaus* is visible in the left background, seemingly overheard by a Moorish kitchen maid, who pauses in her work as though aware of this event. This implies that salvation is possible for her: many Moors converted to Christianity in Spain. This painting was created by Velázquez in Seville at the age of eighteen or nineteen and is considered to be his earliest known picture. It is a *bodegóne,* combining still life and genre in a kitchen or tavern setting. Velázquez captures beautifully the textures of the glazed and burnished vessels, mortar and pestle.

M	T	W	T	F	S	S
26	27	28	29	30	31	1
2	3	4	5	6	7	8
9	10	11	12	13	14	15
16	17	18	19	20	21	22
23	24	25	26	27	28	29
30	31	1	2	3	4	5

January · Eanáir
Week 1 · Seachtain 1

2 Monday · Luan

3 Tuesday · Máirt

4 Wednesday · Céadaoin

5 Thursday · Déardaoin

6 Friday · Aoine

7 Saturday · Satharn

8 Sunday · Domhnach

Marcantonio Bassetti, *Portrait of an Elderly Man,* **1620s**

Following cleaning of this painting in 1968, it was attributed to Macontionio Bassetti, a Veronese artist who worked in Venice and Rome as well as his native city. He is known for his portraits and was considerably influenced by the great Venetian masters of the sixteenth century. This striking portrait has the intense gaze of the sitter found in two portraits by Bassetti in Verona. There are also similarities in the plain background and the precise, tightly painted hair and facial features. His black satin doublet, white collar and brown gloves are plain yet smart.

M	T	W	T	F	S	S
26	27	28	29	30	31	1
2	3	4	5	6	7	8
9	10	11	12	13	14	15
16	17	18	19	20	21	22
23	24	25	26	27	28	29
30	31	1	2	3	4	5

9 Monday · Luan

10 Tuesday · Máirt

11 Wednesday · Céadaoin

12 Thursday · Déardaoin

13 Friday · Aoine

14 Saturday · Satharn

15 Sunday · Domhnach

William Sadler the Younger, *A View of the Pigeon House, Dublin,* **c.1800**

The Pigeon House in Ringsend became a lodging house in 1748, run by an inn-keeper named John Pigeon. Towards the end of the century, with increasing political tensions in Ireland and abroad, it became a military base, providing a landing place for troops. Beside it was a military fort, visible here behind sandbag emplacements and beneath a Union Jack. To the left, yachts are moored, and further out is the Poolbeg Lighthouse, erected in 1762. The route leading to this area is a busy thoroughfare populated with various figures, including soldiers returning to the fort.

M	T	W	T	F	S	S
26	27	28	29	30	31	1
2	3	4	5	6	7	8
9	10	11	12	13	14	15
16	17	18	19	20	21	22
23	24	25	26	27	28	29
30	31	1	2	3	4	5

16 Monday · Luan

17 Tuesday · Máirt

18 Wednesday · Céadaoin

19 Thursday · Déardaoin

20 Friday · Aoine

21 Saturday · Satharn

22 Sunday · Domhnach

Jan Sibrechts, *The Farm Cart,* **1671**

Sibrechts is best known for his picturesque, meticulously painted scenes of Flemish peasants crossing fords with their carts and animals. This is a typical example, depicting a farm cart being led by a boy and horse down a flooded path. The boy and the woman, presumably his mother, gaze out at us. The abundance of fresh vegetables on the cart implies that they are on their way to market in order to sell their produce. They are watched by a dog on a small bridge while cattle, sheep and goats graze and drink close by.

M	T	W	T	F	S	S
26	27	28	29	30	31	1
2	3	4	5	6	7	8
9	10	11	12	13	14	15
16	17	18	19	20	21	22
23	24	25	26	27	28	29
30	31	1	2	3	4	5

January · Eanáir
Week 4 · Seachtain 4

---

23 Monday · Luan

---

24 Tuesday · Máirt

---

25 Wednesday · Céadaoin

---

26 Thursday · Déardaoin

---

27 Friday · Aoine

---

28 Saturday · Satharn

---

29 Sunday · Domhnach

Vincent van Gogh, *Rooftops in Paris,* **1886**

Vincent van Gogh travelled from his native Holland to Paris in early 1886, where he rented an apartment with his brother Theo on the Rue Lepic near Montmartre. This bohemian district of Paris afforded panoramic views of the city, and from his window, Vincent painted four views of the rooftops. This painting, one of the aforementioned series, shows the city centre extending south. The thick application of paint evokes a cloudy, overcast sky.

M	T	W	T	F	S	S
26	27	28	29	30	31	1
2	3	4	5	6	7	8
9	10	11	12	13	14	15
16	17	18	19	20	21	22
23	24	25	26	27	28	29
30	31	1	2	3	4	5

January • Eanáir
Week 5 • Seachtain 5

30 Monday • Luan

31 Tuesday • Máirt

February • Feabhra

1 Wednesday • Céadaoin

2 Thursday • Déardaoin

3 Friday • Aoine

4 Saturday • Satharn

5 Sunday • Domhnach

Hendrik Leys, *A Young Couple,* **1869**

Leys specialised in genre, history paintings and romances, often set in the fifteenth and sixteenth centuries. He depicted period detail and costume with great care and acquired a reputation for historical realism. Here, the young lovers are dressed in early sixteenth-century fashions. The man is more flamboyant, wearing a slashed doublet and hose, a feathered hat and red stockings. He carries a sword and has placed a hunting horn on the ground beside him. His partner, more demure in both her attire and her facial expression, reflects the sombre dignity of many of Leys' characters.

M	T	W	T	F	S	S
26	27	28	29	30	31	1
2	3	4	5	6	7	8
9	10	11	12	13	14	15
16	17	18	19	20	21	22
23	24	25	26	27	28	29
30	31	1	2	3	4	5

February · Feabhra
Week 6 · Seachtain 6

6 Monday · Luan

7 Tuesday · Máirt

8 Wednesday · Céadaoin

9 Thursday · Déardaoin

10 Friday · Aoine

11 Saturday · Satharn

12 Sunday · Domhnach

James Humbert Craig, *The Harbour, Leenane,* **20th century**
Under the influence of French Impressionism, the Irish artist James Humbert Craig became concerned with capturing the fleeting effects of light, while choosing his locations among the numerous bays in the west and south of Ireland. In this painting he focuses on the harbour at Leenane, County Galway: the water, the currachs and the fishermen, their activity not disturbing the calm atmosphere that pervades the scene. Belfast-born Craig exhibited regularly in Dublin, Belfast and London throughout his career and achieved success with his landscapes, favouring those of counties Antrim and Donegal as well as Connemara.

M	T	W	T	F	S	S
30	31	1	2	3	4	5
6	7	8	9	10	11	12
13	14	15	16	17	18	19
20	21	22	23	24	25	26
27	28	1	2	3	4	5

13 Monday · Luan

14 Tuesday · Máirt
St Valentine's Day

15 Wednesday · Céadaoin

16 Thursday · Déardaoin

17 Friday · Aoine

18 Saturday · Satharn

19 Sunday · Domhnach

Daniel Maclise, *Claude Lorrain Sketching,* **1853**

Maclise shows the French landscape painter sketching in the open air, watched by an admiring female companion. By 1626 Claude Lorrain had settled in Rome where he spent much of his time studying the *Campagna*. Maclise may have intended this picture as an ideal representation of the carefree artist. The painting possesses a romantic pastoral quality and is not a portrait of Claude, but rather an imagined portrayal of the artist making a study of a tree against the sky. The bright exuberant faces and meticulous attention to botanical detail are typical of the work of Maclise.

M	T	W	T	F	S	S
30	31	1	2	3	4	5
6	7	8	9	10	11	12
13	14	15	16	17	18	19
20	21	22	23	24	25	26
27	28	1	2	3	4	5

20 Monday · Luan

21 Tuesday · Máirt

22 Wednesday · Céadaoin

23 Thursday · Déardaoin

24 Friday · Aoine

25 Saturday · Satharn

26 Sunday · Domhnach

Mildred Anne Butler, *A View Across Rooftops to ?Newlyn Harbour, Cornwall,* **c.1890s**

Having travelled through France, Butler enrolled at the Newlyn School of Art, Cornwall, where she was introduced to *plein air* and animal painting, in which she became highly skilled. She spent the summers of 1894 and 1895 in Newlyn, where she painted landscapes from unusual, angular perspectives. For this evocative work, she adopts a distinctive high viewpoint among a cluster of rooftops, looking across the smoking chimneys to the harbour and boats beyond. Butler developed a fascination with birds, especially rooks and crows, and enjoyed painting close-up views of them silhouetted against hazy, atmospheric backgrounds.

M	T	W	T	F	S	S
30	31	1	2	3	4	5
6	7	8	9	10	11	12
13	14	15	16	17	18	19
20	21	22	23	24	25	26
27	28	1	2	3	4	5

February · Feabhra
Week 9 · Seachtain 9

27 Monday · Luan

28 Tuesday · Máirt

1 Wednesday · Céadaoin   March · Márta

2 Thursday · Déardaoin

3 Friday · Aoine

4 Saturday · Satharn

5 Sunday · Domhnach

Richard Whately West, *Tête de Chien, Monaco, Winter Sunset,* **19th century**
In the foreground of this dramatic landscape, a path leads towards a descending diagonal line of foreshore with projecting bushes and rocks, while in the distance, the sun sets in a golden sky fleeced with clouds. The light from above is reflected in the rough sea, painted in tones of sapphire, emerald and amethyst. Silhouetted against this intense sunset is the promontory of Tête de Chien, situated in the Alpes-Maritimes in France. This promontory overlooks the principality of Monaco, which is visible nestling below it, painted in the same lilac tones as the clouds above.

M	T	W	T	F	S	S
30	31	1	2	3	4	5
6	7	8	9	10	11	12
13	14	15	16	17	18	19
20	21	22	23	24	25	26
27	28	1	2	3	4	5

March · Márta
Week 10 · Seachtain 10

6 Monday · Luan

7 Tuesday · Máirt

8 Wednesday · Céadaoin

9 Thursday · Déardaoin

10 Friday · Aoine

11 Saturday · Satharn

12 Sunday · Domhnach

Adolf Schreyer, *Arab Horsemen,* **1865/1885**

Schreyer's visits to Syria, Egypt and Algeria informed his colourful scenes, which catered to the French market for Orientalist painting. He made detailed studies of horses and bridles and prided himself on their accuracy, while keeping his locations nondescript. This is a typical example of Schreyer's horsemen who, having perhaps watered their animals, seem ready to set out again. The rider in the centre, astride his white steed, may be the leader. He sits back in his saddle with confidence, anchoring the composition, while around him the other riders attend to their frisky horses.

M	T	W	T	F	S	S
27	28	1	2	3	4	5
6	7	8	9	10	11	12
13	14	15	16	17	18	19
20	21	22	23	24	25	26
27	28	29	30	31	1	2

March · Márta
Week 11 · Seachtain 11

13 Monday · Luan

14 Tuesday · Máirt

15 Wednesday · Céadaoin

16 Thursday · Déardaoin

17 Friday · Aoine
St Patrick's Day

18 Saturday · Satharn

19 Sunday · Domhnach

Erskine Nichol, *The 16th, 17th (St Patrick's Day) and 18th March,* **1856**

This large, detailed picture and its title imply that St Patrick's Day was a drawn-out, three-day festival featuring dancing, courting, music making, storytelling, eating, drinking and hawking. In reality, it was, for most Irish people in the mid-nineteenth century, a holy day on the liturgical calendar and was not declared a national holiday until 1900. However, Nichol has chosen to depict St Patrick's Day as an opportunity for revelry rather than worship. The church, St Doulough's near Malahide, appears to be closed, while the pub nearby attracts the business of the colourfully dressed peasants celebrating outside.

M	T	W	T	F	S	S
27	28	1	2	3	4	5
6	7	8	9	10	11	12
13	14	15	16	17	18	19
20	21	22	23	24	25	26
27	28	29	30	31	1	2

20 Monday · Luan

21 Tuesday · Máirt

22 Wednesday · Céadaoin

23 Thursday · Déardaoin

24 Friday · Aoine

25 Saturday · Satharn

26 Sunday · Domhnach

Mothering Sunday

Samuel Lover, *Mrs Lover and her Daughter,* **1830**

Lover had numerous talents as a singer, novelist, songwriter, musician, waltzer and artist. He performed as the personification of the stage-Irishman in music-halls, becoming popular in Dublin and London society. This portrait of the artist's wife and daughter was painted three years after their marriage. Mrs Lover wears a wide-brimmed hat festooned with ostrich feathers, a dark cape and a satin dress with lace collar. She admires her tiny baby, who sits upright on a stone balustrade. They are framed by colourful flowers in the top left and a potted lily in the lower right.

M	T	W	T	F	S	S
27	28	1	2	3	4	5
6	7	8	9	10	11	12
13	14	15	16	17	18	19
20	21	22	23	24	25	26
27	28	29	30	31	1	2

27 Monday · Luan

28 Tuesday · Máirt

29 Wednesday · Céadaoin

30 Thursday · Déardaoin

31 Friday · Aoine

1 Saturday · Satharn

April · Aibreán

2 Sunday · Domhnach

Gabriel Metsu, *Man Writing a Letter,* **c.1664–1666**

A gentleman wearing a black silk suit with white linen shirt writes a letter at a table covered with an imported Persian carpet. His wide-brimmed hat hangs on the back of a red upholstered chair. The furnishings, silver inkstand and elegant interior suggest this man's affluence. Behind the panes of an open window, a globe signifies his worldly pursuit; he may be a merchant or a learned and well-travelled man. This painting and *Woman Reading a Letter* (overleaf) were intended by Metsu as pendants and depict the exchange of a love letter between an Amsterdam couple.

M	T	W	T	F	S	S
27	28	1	2	3	4	5
6	7	8	9	10	11	12
13	14	15	16	17	18	19
20	21	22	23	24	25	26
27	28	29	30	31	1	2

3 Monday · Luan

4 Tuesday · Máirt

5 Wednesday · Céadaoin

6 Thursday · Déardaoin

7 Friday · Aoine

8 Saturday · Satharn

9 Sunday · Domhnach

Gabriel Metsu, *Woman Reading a Letter,* **c.1664–1666**
A lady wearing an ermine-trimmed jacket reads a letter by a window. Her relationship to its sender is suggested by the spaniel, symbolic of fidelity, the bucket decorated with Cupid's arrows and the cast-off shoe, which has erotic connotations in art. The curl on the lady's forehead indicates her engaged status, while a mirror behind her warns against vanity. An abandoned sewing basket and a discarded thimble on the floor suggest that she has forgotten her domestic chores. A maid reveals a picture of a ship in a stormy sea, perhaps a metaphor for romance.

M	T	W	T	F	S	S
27	28	29	30	31	1	2
3	4	5	6	7	8	9
10	11	12	13	14	15	16
17	18	19	20	21	22	23
24	25	26	27	28	29	30

April · Aibreán
Week 15 · Seachtain 15

10 Monday · Luan

11 Tuesday · Máirt

12 Wednesday · Céadaoin

13 Thursday · Déardaoin

14 Friday · Aoine
Good Friday

15 Saturday · Satharn

16 Sunday · Domhnach
Easter

John George Mulvany, *A Kitchen Interior,* **19th century**

Mulvany exhibited in Dublin from 1810 and was invited to become a founder member of the Royal Hibernian Academy on its establishment in 1823. He specialised in landscapes and rural scenes, often with anecdotal detail, such as people and animals, which inject life into his paintings. His paintings possess a charming naiveté apparent in this quaint domestic scene of the interior of the home of a fairly prosperous Irish tenant farmer in the 1798 period. The relative scale of the figures is disconcerting, but this is compensated by Mulvany's attention to detail in the furnishings.

M	T	W	T	F	S	S
27	28	29	30	31	1	2
3	4	5	6	7	8	9
10	11	12	13	14	15	16
17	18	19	20	21	22	23
24	25	26	27	28	29	30

April • Aibreán
Week 16 • Seachtain 16

17 Monday • Luan
Easter Monday

18 Tuesday • Máirt

19 Wednesday • Céadaoin

20 Thursday • Déardaoin

21 Friday • Aoine

22 Saturday • Satharn

23 Sunday • Domhnach

Maerten de Vos, *The Resurrection of Christ,* **c.1564**

Having come under the influence of Tintoretto in Italy, de Vos returned to his native Antwerp where he became the most important artist of the Mannerist period. De Vos specialised in monumental altarpieces painted in a vigorous, eccentric style, as exemplified by this large example of the artist's early work. The resurrection of Christ was a popular subject in sixteenth-century Netherlandish art. In this dramatic interpretation, the earthly figures are typically Mannerist with elongated, disproportionate bodies and awkward, contorted poses. The figure of Christ, by contrast, is serenely elegant in pose and classical in style.

M	T	W	T	F	S	S
27	28	29	30	31	1	2
3	4	5	6	7	8	9
10	11	12	13	14	15	16
17	18	19	20	21	22	23
24	25	26	27	28	29	30

24 Monday · Luan

25 Tuesday · Máirt

26 Wednesday · Céadaoin

27 Thursday · Déardaoin

28 Friday · Aoine

29 Saturday · Satharn

30 Sunday · Domhnach

François Bunel the Younger, *The Procession of the League,* **c.1590**

The Procession of the League took place in Paris on 5 June 1590. After the death in May 1590 of Cardinal de Bourbon, who had been recognised as King Charles X by the Catholic League, the latter reinforced their efforts to prevent a heretic (Henry IV) from taking over the now vacant throne. The League members, including priests and monks of various orders, arranged a procession through the streets of Paris, armed with halberds and muskets. A group of aldermen, dressed in black, stand under the canopy of a shop as two demonstrators fire their muskets.

M	T	W	T	F	S	S
27	28	29	30	31	1	2
3	4	5	6	7	8	9
10	11	12	13	14	15	16
17	18	19	20	21	22	23
24	25	26	27	28	29	30

May · Bealtaine
Week 18 · Seachtain 18

1 Monday · Luan May · Bealtaine
Bank Holiday (RoI and NI)

---

2 Tuesday · Máirt

---

3 Wednesday · Céadaoin

---

4 Thursday · Déardaoin

---

5 Friday · Aoine

---

6 Saturday · Satharn

---

7 Sunday · Domhnach

Cornelis Bega, *Two Men Singing,* **1662**

Bega specialised in painting the Dutch middle and lower classes in domestic interiors and taverns, and he frequently included drunkards, gamblers, alchemists, prostitutes or nursing mothers. In this typical scene, two men sing a ballad from a music sheet, surrounded by peeling leather-bound books and fabrics, all shown in disarray. In the foreground a large four-stringed violincello known as a *basse de violon* leans against a box. The setting resembles a thieves' lair and the men's occupations remain uncertain; however, their attire would imply that they do not belong to the peasant class.

M	T	W	T	F	S	S
1	2	3	4	5	6	7
8	9	10	11	12	13	14
15	16	17	18	19	20	21
22	23	24	25	26	27	28
29	30	31	1	2	3	4

May • Bealtaine
Week 19 • Seachtain 19

8 Monday • Luan

9 Tuesday • Máirt

10 Wednesday • Céadaoin

11 Thursday • Déardaoin

12 Friday • Aoine

13 Saturday • Satharn

14 Sunday • Domhnach

William Orpen, *Portrait of Augusta Gregory, Dramatist,* **20th century**
Augusta Gregory (1852–1932) was wife of Sir William Gregory of Coole Park, County Galway, to which she welcomed the leaders of the Irish Literary Revival including W.B. Yeats, Edward Martyn, Douglas Hyde, Seán O'Casey, George Bernard Shaw and J.M. Synge. These gatherings led to the creation of the Irish Literary Theatre and the Abbey Theatre, of which Lady Gregory was a co-founder and co-director. She learned Irish, became a keen nationalist, folklorist and dramatist, and helped Douglas Hyde found a branch of the Gaelic League at Kiltartan, near Coole. This forceful portrait was commissioned from William Orpen by Hugh Lane.

M	T	W	T	F	S	S
1	2	3	4	5	6	7
8	9	10	11	12	13	14
15	16	17	18	19	20	21
22	23	24	25	26	27	28
29	30	31	1	2	3	4

May · Bealtaine
Week 20 · Seachtain 20

15 Monday · Luan

16 Tuesday · Máirt

17 Wednesday · Céadaoin

18 Thursday · Déardaoin

19 Friday · Aoine

20 Saturday · Satharn

21 Sunday · Domhnach

Edouard Vuillard, *The Hessels' Apartment, rue de Rivoli, Paris,* **1903**

In 1900 Vuillard embarked upon a close friendship with Lucy Hessel, wife of Jos Hessel, Vuillard's new art dealer at the Bernheim-Jeune Gallery in Paris. Their relationship lasted for the next forty years and provided a new impetus to Vuillard's art, with Lucy adopting the role of muse. Vuillard visited the Hessels' apartment with such regularity in the early 1900s that their servants called him the 'house painter'. This loose sketch in gouache depicts Lucy in her dressing room, seated with her back to the viewer, in the presence of a man (most likely her husband).

M	T	W	T	F	S	S
1	2	3	4	5	6	7
8	9	10	11	12	13	14
15	16	17	18	19	20	21
22	23	24	25	26	27	28
29	30	31	1	2	3	4

22 Monday · Luan

23 Tuesday · Máirt

24 Wednesday · Céadaoin

25 Thursday · Déardaoin

26 Friday · Aoine

27 Saturday · Satharn

28 Sunday · Domhnach

Aelbert Cuyp, *Landscape with a Portrait of a Youth and his Tutor on Horseback,* **c.1650–1652**
An aristocratic young man wearing a purple velvet riding tunic trimmed with fur cocks his right elbow, emphasising its slashed design. An older gentleman, most likely his tutor, wears a navy tunic trimmed with gold braid. Both wear plumed hats as they halt during a hunt. Their lavish garments may have been props drawn from the artist's studio. Cuyp often used rich or exotic costumes to lend his hunting scenes the gravitas of history painting. Horsemanship and hunting were essential components of noble life and of the education of young men in seventeenth-century Holland.

M	T	W	T	F	S	S
1	2	3	4	5	6	7
8	9	10	11	12	13	14
15	16	17	18	19	20	21
22	23	24	25	26	27	28
29	30	31	1	2	3	4

May · Bealtaine
Week 22 · Seachtain 22

29 Monday · Luan
Bank Holiday (NI)

30 Tuesday · Máirt

31 Wednesday · Céadaoin

1 Thursday · Déardaoin   June · Meitheamh

2 Friday · Aoine

3 Saturday · Satharn

4 Sunday · Domhnach

William Scott, *Mackerel and Bottle,* **c.1949**

Scott was attracted to the shapes, textures and contours of everyday objects. His minimal, understated still life paintings display arrangements of pots, pans, fish and bottles that appear to float above bare kitchen tables, whose surfaces seems tipped up towards the viewer. By his own admission, Scott was uninterested in the objects themselves. Rather, it was their banality that rendered them ideal: they provided a contrast of forms without distracting associations. These objects create a near-abstract arrangement against the empty background. Scott aimed to make his pictures uncontrived with an immediacy akin to children's art.

M	T	W	T	F	S	S
1	2	3	4	5	6	7
8	9	10	11	12	13	14
15	16	17	18	19	20	21
22	23	24	25	26	27	28
29	30	31	1	2	3	4

5 Monday · Luan
Bank Holiday (RoI)

---

6 Tuesday · Máirt

---

7 Wednesday · Céadaoin

---

8 Thursday · Déardaoin

---

9 Friday · Aoine

---

10 Saturday · Satharn

---

11 Sunday · Domhnach

Mary Swanzy, *A Figure Study,* **mid-20th century**
The Second World War greatly impacted on Swanzy's art, which became tinged with foreboding and despair.
Rather than creating frontline images of battle, she chose to reflect on the effect of war on the psyche, the
imminence of war and its consequent ravages on humanity. Allegory and symbolism take on a new role
in this highly personalised, Expressionist painting, in which Swanzy subtly layers and blends colours with a
swirling, fragmented light. The ominous note present in paintings such as this is typical of her wartime work,
in which the full meaning often remains unclear.

M	T	W	T	F	S	S
29	30	31	1	2	3	4
5	6	7	8	9	10	11
12	13	14	15	16	17	18
19	20	21	22	23	24	25
26	27	28	29	30	1	2

June · Meitheamh
Week 24 · Seachtain 24

12 Monday · Luan

13 Tuesday · Máirt

14 Wednesday · Céadaoin

15 Thursday · Déardaoin

16 Friday · Aoine

17 Saturday · Satharn

18 Sunday · Domhnach
Fathers' Day

William Evans of Eton, *Buttermilk Lane, Galway,* **1838**

In the 1830s the English artist William Evans, drawing master at Eton College, made two tours of Connemara, then a barely navigable area in the west of Ireland, also visiting Galway city. This watercolour view of Buttermilk Lane was made on his second visit in 1838. Here the pale spire of St. Nicholas' Church is visible beyond the High Street archway. Evans records women in colourful peasant garb as they chat or attempt to sell their produce, while washing hangs above their heads on poles. This late fifteenth-century laneway survives to this day.

M	T	W	T	F	S	S
29	30	31	1	2	3	4
5	6	7	8	9	10	11
12	13	14	15	16	17	18
19	20	21	22	23	24	25
26	27	28	29	30	1	2

June • Meitheamh
Week 25 • Seachtain 25

19 Monday • Luan

20 Tuesday • Máirt

21 Wednesday • Céadaoin

22 Thursday • Déardaoin

23 Friday • Aoine

24 Saturday • Satharn

25 Sunday • Domhnach

William John Leech, *A Still Afternoon, Concarneau,* **c.1910**

Leech discovered the Breton medieval walled town of Concarneau in 1903, returning frequently thereafter. Among the scenes he created there were studies of different times of the day, painted in muted blue tones. Some of these possess an almost palpable feeling of sunlight and shadow, which could only have been achieved by painting *en plein air* (outside). Leech also studied flattened patterns of reflections on water as seen from above, as in the high vantage point adopted for this calm view of a pool of water framed by a vertical tree trunk and diagonal branches.

M	T	W	T	F	S	S
29	30	31	1	2	3	4
5	6	7	8	9	10	11
12	13	14	15	16	17	18
19	20	21	22	23	24	25
26	27	28	29	30	1	2

26 Monday • Luan

27 Tuesday • Máirt

28 Wednesday • Céadaoin

29 Thursday • Déardaoin

30 Friday • Aoine

1 Saturday • Satharn   July • Iúil

2 Sunday • Domhnach

Rosalba Carriera, *Summer,* **1720s–1730s**

Carriera influenced a generation of artists in France and England in the art of pastel. Settling in Paris, she worked for the court and aristocratic patrons. She created several pastels representing the seasons, mostly during the 1720s and 1730s. Her diaries reveal that she began one set in 1725, the year in which Vivaldi's *The Four Seasons* had its first advertised performance. Carriera depicts the seasons as women adorned with traditional seasonal attributes. Flowers and ears of corn identify this figure as Summer, whose pale complexion, lightly rouged cheeks and dark eyes are enhanced by pearl earrings.

M	T	W	T	F	S	S
29	30	31	1	2	3	4
5	6	7	8	9	10	11
12	13	14	15	16	17	18
19	20	21	22	23	24	25
26	27	28	29	30	1	2

July · Iúil
Week 27 · Seachtain 27

3 Monday · Luan

4 Tuesday · Máirt

5 Wednesday · Céadaoin

6 Thursday · Déardaoin

7 Friday · Aoine

8 Saturday · Satharn

9 Sunday · Domhnach

Andrew Nicholl, *Londonderry on the River Foyle, County Derry, Beyond a Bank of Flowers,* **1870**

Nicholl was a painter of topographical views and of flowers and plants, subjects that he combined in a number of detailed watercolours. Here he sets a vivid bank of wild flowers against a distant view of the city of Derry. Nicholl's talent as a botanical artist is evident in the crisply painted poppies, cornflowers, forget-me-nots and daisies. He shows his topographical skill, meanwhile, in his recording of the Cathedral Church of St Colum to the left, the Carlisle Bridge in the centre, spanning the River Foyle, and the Church of All Saints to the right.

M	T	W	T	F	S	S
26	27	28	29	30	1	2
3	4	5	6	7	8	9
10	11	12	13	14	15	16
17	18	19	20	21	22	23
24	25	26	27	28	29	30
31	1	2	3	4	5	6

10 Monday · Luan

11 Tuesday · Máirt

12 Wednesday · Céadaoin
Bank Holiday (NI)

13 Thursday · Déardaoin

14 Friday · Aoine

15 Saturday · Satharn

16 Sunday · Domhnach

Roderic O'Conor, *Landscape with Rocks,* **c.1913**

In this seascape of foreground rocks and distant headland bathed in bright sunshine, O'Conor's short, directional brushstrokes and use of pure, vivid colour reveal the impact of Fauvism. In southern France he came under the influence of the Fauve painters Henri Matisse, André Derain and Maurice de Vlaminck, who had all painted in Cassis near Marseilles. This may have been the impetus for O'Conor to rent a villa there in 1913 and to immerse himself in painting local landscapes, his brushwork becoming loose and sketchy in the southern light.

M	T	W	T	F	S	S
26	27	28	29	30	1	2
3	4	5	6	7	8	9
10	11	12	13	14	15	16
17	18	19	20	21	22	23
24	25	26	27	28	29	30
31	1	2	3	4	5	6

July · Iúil
Week 29 · Seachtain 29

17 Monday · Luan

18 Tuesday · Máirt

19 Wednesday · Céadaoin

20 Thursday · Déardaoin

21 Friday · Aoine

22 Saturday · Satharn

23 Sunday · Domhnach

Baron François Gérard, *Marie-Julie Bonaparte as Queen of Spain with her Daughters, Zénaide and Charlotte,* **1808–1809**

As principal portraitist to Napoleon I, Gérard painted many members of the Bonaparte family. Marie-Julie Clary married Napoleon's brother Joseph, who in 1808 became king of Spain. Dressed as his queen, she wears a white satin empire-line gown with gold lamé foliage at the hemline, which is repeated on her red velvet overcape. Her shoulders are adorned with transparent fairy-ring epaulettes. Her daughters wear pink muslin and voile dresses and satin pumps. The neoclassical furnishings in this elegant interior and the grounds outside may belong to the Château of Mortefontaine, Joseph Bonaparte's residence outside Paris.

M	T	W	T	F	S	S
26	27	28	29	30	1	2
3	4	5	6	7	8	9
10	11	12	13	14	15	16
17	18	19	20	21	22	23
24	25	26	27	28	29	30
31	1	2	3	4	5	6

July · Iúil
Week 30 · Seachtain 30

24 Monday · Luan

25 Tuesday · Máirt

26 Wednesday · Céadaoin

27 Thursday · Déardaoin

28 Friday · Aoine

29 Saturday · Satharn

30 Sunday · Domhnach

Thomas Gainsborough, *The Cottage Girl,* **1785**

A child in ragged clothing has come from a cottage to take water from a brook. She stands forlornly, holding a broken earthenware pitcher in one hand and a dog in the other. During the 1780s, Gainsborough painted almost twenty 'fancy pictures' of rustic figures, often children, set in Arcadian, imaginary landscapes. These emotive works struck a deep chord with the British public, appealing to the contemporary taste in art, literature and gardening for picturesque rural idylls, at a time when the poetry of William Wordsworth was gaining popularity.

M	T	W	T	F	S	S
26	27	28	29	30	1	2
3	4	5	6	7	8	9
10	11	12	13	14	15	16
17	18	19	20	21	22	23
24	25	26	27	28	29	30
31	1	2	3	4	5	6

31 Monday · Luan

1 Tuesday · Máirt   August · Lúnasa

2 Wednesday · Céadaoin

3 Thursday · Déardaoin

4 Friday · Aoine

5 Saturday · Satharn

6 Sunday · Domhnach

Vincenzo di Biagio Catena and unknown artist, Ireland, *Portrait of two Venetian Gentlemen,* **c.1510 and 18th century**

These two men appear unaware of and do not interact with each other. The young man on the right, wearing the robes of a religious confraternity, is attributed to Catena, who was active in Venice in the early 1500s. The older man on the left, perhaps a member of the Venetian oligarchy, is thought to have been painted by a later Irish artist. He is painted with a looser style of brushwork that Catena never achieved. He appears more senior in rank and age and wears more sumptuous attire of ermine and cloth of gold.

M	T	W	T	F	S	S
26	27	28	29	30	1	2
3	4	5	6	7	8	9
10	11	12	13	14	15	16
17	18	19	20	21	22	23
24	25	26	27	28	29	30
31	1	2	3	4	5	6

August · Lúnasa
Week 32 · Seachtain 32

7 Monday · Luan
Bank Holiday (RoI)

8 Tuesday · Máirt

9 Wednesday · Céadaoin

10 Thursday · Déardaoin

11 Friday · Aoine

12 Saturday · Satharn

13 Sunday · Domhnach

James Holland, *Flowers in a Bowl,* **1865**

A selection of brightly hued flowers and foliage is displayed in a low oval dish, painted white with a blue band. Some petals have fallen onto the table. Born in Burslem, Staffordshire, into a family who were employed as painters at a local pottery works, Holland also worked there from the age of twelve, painting flowers on pottery and porcelain. In London, he became known as a painter of flowers, landscapes, architecture and marine subjects in oil and watercolour. He was known for his skill as a colourist, as is evident in this cheerful watercolour.

M	T	W	T	F	S	S
31	1	2	3	4	5	6
7	8	9	10	11	12	13
14	15	16	17	18	19	20
21	22	23	24	25	26	27
28	29	30	31	1	2	3

14 Monday · Luan

15 Tuesday · Máirt

16 Wednesday · Céadaoin

17 Thursday · Déardaoin

18 Friday · Aoine

19 Saturday · Satharn

20 Sunday · Domhnach

Bartolomé Esteban Murillo, *The Departure of the Prodigal Son,* **1660s**

The Gospel of St Luke tells the parable of the prodigal son, in which the younger son of a wealthy father demands his inheritance before leaving the family home. Murillo set the story in contemporary Seville in a series of six canvases, which have the appearance of genre scenes rather than religious subjects. In The Departure, the distraught family gathers on the steps to bid farewell to their son. Their sombre clothing contrasts with the son's brilliant scarlet cloak as, mounted on a fine horse, he prepares to join the heavily laden pack-mules that have set off before him.

M	T	W	T	F	S	S
31	1	2	3	4	5	6
7	8	9	10	11	12	13
14	15	16	17	18	19	20
21	22	23	24	25	26	27
28	29	30	31	1	2	3

August · Lúnasa
Week 34 · Seachtain 34

21 Monday · Luan

22 Tuesday · Máirt

23 Wednesday · Céadaoin

24 Thursday · Déardaoin

25 Friday · Aoine

26 Saturday · Satharn

27 Sunday · Domhnach

Follower of Rembrandt van Rijn, *Head of an Old Man,* **c.1644–1650**

When acquired by the National Gallery, this picture was considered a Rembrandt and was dated by most authorities to c.1650. Later, it was believed by some to be a nineteenth-century forgery. Restoration work and dendrochronological tests in 1998 established that it was painted on a wooden panel dating from c.1644-1650. The technique is consistent with seventeenth-century practice, evident in the execution of the old man's face, beard and skull cap. Recent opinion is that it is a Dutch picture of the seventeenth century, very close to Rembrandt, perhaps by a pupil working in his studio.

M	T	W	T	F	S	S
31	1	2	3	4	5	6
7	8	9	10	11	12	13
14	15	16	17	18	19	20
21	22	23	24	25	26	27
28	29	30	31	1	2	3

August · Lúnasa
Week 35 · Seachtain 35

28 Monday · Luan
Bank Holiday (NI)

29 Tuesday · Máirt

30 Wednesday · Céadaoin

31 Thursday · Déardaoin

1 Friday · Aoine   September · Meán Fómhair

2 Saturday · Satharn

3 Sunday · Domhnach

Frederic William Burton, *Portrait of Miss Annie Callwell (d.1904),* **late 1840s**

Annie Callwell was the daughter of Robert Callwell, who served on the first Board of the National Gallery of Ireland. He and Burton became acquainted in 1843 when they sat on a committee to found the National Gallery. Burton has painted Annie Callwell against a wooded landscape, surrounded by flowers and leaves. Her wistful expression and the profuse depiction of nature lend the painting a romantic air. Burton usually employed watercolour in a dense, meticulous technique, but the looseness of his handling in the foliage and dress may indicate that this is an unfinished work.

M	T	W	T	F	S	S
31	1	2	3	4	5	6
7	8	9	10	11	12	13
14	15	16	17	18	19	20
21	22	23	24	25	26	27
28	29	30	31	1	2	3

September · Meán Fómhair
Week 36 · Seachtain 36

4 Monday · Luan

5 Tuesday · Máirt

6 Wednesday · Céadaoin

7 Thursday · Déardaoin

8 Friday · Aoine

9 Saturday · Satharn

10 Sunday · Domhnach

John Lavery, *On the Bridge at Grez,* **1884**

The old stone bridge was a landmark of Grez-sur-Loing, a Breton village which was popular among artists in the mid-nineteenth century. The bridge was painted by most artists who stayed there. Lavery's view is more unusual, as it is a view *on* the bridge, rather that *of* it. The young man leaning against it, with his equipment by his side, is almost certainly the Irish painter Frank O'Meara, whom Lavery greatly admired. O'Meara was a key member of the artistic community in Grez, and his relaxed pose epitomises the easy pace of life there.

M	T	W	T	F	S	S
28	29	30	31	1	2	3
4	5	6	7	8	9	10
11	12	13	14	15	16	17
18	19	20	21	22	23	24
25	26	27	28	29	30	1

September · Meán Fómhair
Week 37 · Seachtain 37

11 Monday · Luan

12 Tuesday · Máirt

13 Wednesday · Céadaoin

14 Thursday · Déardaoin

15 Friday · Aoine

16 Saturday · Satharn

17 Sunday · Domhnach

Joseph Malachy Kavanagh, *Sheep in a Landscape,* **late 19th/early 20th century**
Kavanagh studied in Antwerp with fellow Irish artists Walter Osborne and Nathaniel Hill before moving to Brittany and Normandy, and finally returning to Ireland. In Dublin, he taught at the Royal Hibernian Academy School of Art, becoming a member and later, its Keeper. Kavanagh was a skilled landscape painter, influenced by French *plein air* painting and Dutch Naturalism. He successfully captured light and weather effects in quiet, peaceful scenes such as this view of sheep grazing on a field. Behind the animals, white clouds in a blue sky meet the field at a hard horizon line.

M	T	W	T	F	S	S
28	29	30	31	1	2	3
4	5	6	7	8	9	10
11	12	13	14	15	16	17
18	19	20	21	22	23	24
25	26	27	28	29	30	1

September · Meán Fómhair
Week 38 · Seachtain 38

18 Monday · Luan

19 Tuesday · Máirt

20 Wednesday · Céadaoin

21 Thursday · Déardaoin

22 Friday · Aoine

23 Saturday · Satharn

24 Sunday · Domhnach

Thomas Hickey, *An Indian Lady, perhaps 'Jemdanee', Bibi of William Hickey,* **1787**

From 1784 to 1824 Thomas Hickey lived in India, where he painted portraits of the expatriot British community. In Calcutta he was befriended by the attorney and diarist William Hickey (no relation), who became his patron. This haunting portrait, one of Thomas Hickey's finest, is of a beautiful young Bengali Muslim woman, thought to be Bibi Jemdanee, the mistress of William Hickey. She wears a fine pink muslin sari, fringed with gold thread, a pale pink muslin skirt, loose green trousers, or *salwar*, and gold and silver jewellery on her hair, forehead, ears, neck, wrist and ankle.

M	T	W	T	F	S	S
28	29	30	31	1	2	3
4	5	6	7	8	9	10
11	12	13	14	15	16	17
18	19	20	21	22	23	24
25	26	27	28	29	30	1

September · Meán Fómhair
Week 39 · Seachtain 39

25 Monday · Luan

26 Tuesday · Máirt

27 Wednesday · Céadaoin

28 Thursday · Déardaoin

29 Friday · Aoine

30 Saturday · Satharn

1 Sunday · Domhnach   October · Deireadh Fómhair

George Petrie, *The Stone Circle on Caan Hill, County Derry,* **1840**

While several stone circles in County Derry have been destroyed, a partial one exists at Templemoyle Caugh, near Dungiven, which may be the location of this watercolour. One stone rises up against the evening sky, in which a star shines brightly. Cattle stand motionless on the horizon line, silhouetted against the sunset. Petrie had a deep interest in Irish antiquities and spent much of his life visiting archaeological sites, recording ancient monuments with accuracy and commenting on their origins and uses. A versatile character, Petrie was a painter, antiquarian, musician, writer and a collector of folklore.

M	T	W	T	F	S	S
28	29	30	31	1	2	3
4	5	6	7	8	9	10
11	12	13	14	15	16	17
18	19	20	21	22	23	24
25	26	27	28	29	30	1

October · Deireadh Fómhair
Week 40 · Seachtain 40

2 Monday · Luan

3 Tuesday · Máirt

4 Wednesday · Céadaoin

5 Thursday · Déardaoin

6 Friday · Aoine

7 Saturday · Satharn

8 Sunday · Domhnach

Harry Clarke, *The Tinderbox,* **1916**

The Tinderbox, one of Hans Christian Andersen's first fairy tales, has similarities to *Aladdin and the Magic Lamp*. It tells the story of a soldier who acquires a magic tinderbox capable of summoning three powerful dogs to do the owner's bidding. The soldier is sentenced to death by the king, but by striking the tinderbox with fire, the soldier summons the dogs, who grant his wish and save his life. The soldier is shown arriving to a chamber filled with precious coins, guarded by a dog with 'eyes as big as teacups staring at him'.

M	T	W	T	F	S	S
25	26	27	28	29	30	1
2	3	4	5	6	7	8
9	10	11	12	13	14	15
16	17	18	19	20	21	22
23	24	25	26	27	28	29
30	31	1	2	3	4	5

9 Monday • Luan

10 Tuesday • Máirt

11 Wednesday • Céadaoin

12 Thursday • Déardaoin

13 Friday • Aoine

14 Saturday • Satharn

15 Sunday • Domhnach

Roderic O'Conor, *A Quiet Read,* **c.1907–1908**

In this informal glimpse of a woman reading a book on a chaise longue, O'Conor creates spatial ambiguity by placing a large mirror behind the model; this also allows him to explore the qualities of light and shade in the picture space. By positioning the girl in front of the mirror, O'Conor sets up an interesting visual interplay between the real and the reflected image in this interior scene. His thin washes of blue, mauve and pink, allowing patches of bare canvas to show through in places, give the impression of a quickly executed sketch.

M	T	W	T	F	S	S
25	26	27	28	29	30	1
2	3	4	5	6	7	8
9	10	11	12	13	14	15
16	17	18	19	20	21	22
23	24	25	26	27	28	29
30	31	1	2	3	4	5

16 Monday · Luan

17 Tuesday · Máirt

18 Wednesday · Céadaoin

19 Thursday · Déardaoin

20 Friday · Aoine

21 Saturday · Satharn

22 Sunday · Domhnach

Anton Raphael Mengs, *Portrait of Thomas Connolly (1738–1803),* **1758**

Connolly posed for this portrait during his grand tour of Rome. His frockcoat and waistcoat are trimmed with gold braid and he stands at the base of a Doric column, gesturing to a marble relief depicting three of the nine Muses, who represented the highest artistic and intellectual aspirations. This relief is taken from a sarcophagus now in the Louvre Museum, Paris, and reminds us of the educational purpose of Connolly's visit to Rome. His home, Castletown House, County Kildare, one of the finest neo-Palladian mansions in Ireland, was built for his grand-uncle, William Connolly.

M	T	W	T	F	S	S
25	26	27	28	29	30	1
2	3	4	5	6	7	8
9	10	11	12	13	14	15
16	17	18	19	20	21	22
23	24	25	26	27	28	29
30	31	1	2	3	4	5

October · Deireadh Fómhair
Week 43 · Seachtain 43

23 Monday · Luan

24 Tuesday · Máirt

25 Wednesday · Céadaoin

26 Thursday · Déardaoin

27 Friday · Aoine

28 Saturday · Satharn

29 Sunday · Domhnach

Guercino, *The Virgin and Child (for the Madonna del Carmine Presenting a Scapular to a Carmelite, in Cento's Pinacoteca Civica),* **c.1615**

This is a preparatory drawing for an altarpiece now in the Pinacoteca Civica at Cento, Guercino's home town in northern Italy. The Madonna del Carmine (Our Lady of Mount Carmel) is shown with the Christ Child presenting a scapular to the Carmelite monk St Albert. A scapular is a type of apron originally worn by monks, consisting of pieces of cloth worn front and back, joined by straps over the shoulders. It forms part of the habit of some religious orders including the Carmelites, for whom it remains a sign of Mary's motherly protection.

M	T	W	T	F	S	S
25	26	27	28	29	30	1
2	3	4	5	6	7	8
9	10	11	12	13	14	15
16	17	18	19	20	21	22
23	24	25	26	27	28	29
30	31	1	2	3	4	5

October · Deireadh Fómhair
Week 44 · Seachtain 44

30 Monday · Luan
Bank Holiday (RoI)

31 Tuesday · Máirt

1 Wednesday · Céadaoin   November · Samhain

2 Thursday · Déardaoin

3 Friday · Aoine

4 Saturday · Satharn

5 Sunday · Domhnach

Edwin Henry Landseer, *A King Charles Spaniel,* **1840s**

Landseer was Queen Victoria's favourite painter. He specialised in portraying animals in a somewhat
sentimental light and often gave them semi-human expressions, which secured his popularity during an era
when sensibilities were all important. This small painting was produced for Landseer's patron, Robert Vernon,
and is reported to have been created in one or two days. The spaniel's round face and eyes are echoed in the
circular format of the picture, while its gentle, innocent expression epitomises the popular image of such a
domestic animal, that of complete devotion to its master.

M	T	W	T	F	S	S
25	26	27	28	29	30	1
2	3	4	5	6	7	8
9	10	11	12	13	14	15
16	17	18	19	20	21	22
23	24	25	26	27	28	29
30	31	1	2	3	4	5

6 Monday · Luan

7 Tuesday · Máirt

8 Wednesday · Céadaoin

9 Thursday · Déardaoin

10 Friday · Aoine

11 Saturday · Satharn

12 Sunday · Domhnach

Roderic O'Conor, *Portrait of a Man, possibly Paul Serusier,* **1895**

During the 1890s in Paris and in Brittany, O'Conor thoroughly explored the technique of etching, making etchings on thin zinc sheets. Only a small number of proofs were made, making his prints extremely rare. This print is signed and dated 1895 and is thought to be a portrait of fellow artist Paul Serusier, whom O'Conor met and become close friends with in Brittany at this time. It is a powerful portrait and a very rare impression, printed with a rich plate tone and vivid rendering, revealing the artist's direct, rhythmic and expressive use of line.

M	T	W	T	F	S	S
30	31	1	2	3	4	5
6	7	8	9	10	11	12
13	14	15	16	17	18	19
20	21	22	23	24	25	26
27	28	29	30	1	2	3

November · Samhain
Week 46 · Seachtain 46

13 Monday · Luan

14 Tuesday · Máirt

15 Wednesday · Céadaoin

16 Thursday · Déardaoin

17 Friday · Aoine

18 Saturday · Satharn

19 Sunday · Domhnach

Andries Vermeulen, *Scene on the Ice,* **18th/19th century**

The eighteenth-century artist Vermeulen was born in Dordrecht, where he trained with his father. He painted marine and winter landscapes such as this frosty scene of Dutch peasants going about their daily chores in a land which was at that time mostly covered with snow and ice in winter. Although similar in style, Vermeulen did not in fact belong to the Golden Age of Dutch painting of the seventeenth century. Later artists like him imitated the work of their eminent predecessors and, to the inexperienced eye, it is often difficult to differentiate between seventeenth-century paintings and later variants.

M	T	W	T	F	S	S
30	31	1	2	3	4	5
6	7	8	9	10	11	12
13	14	15	16	17	18	19
20	21	22	23	24	25	26
27	28	29	30	1	2	3

20 Monday · Luan

21 Tuesday · Máirt

22 Wednesday · Céadaoin

23 Thursday · Déardaoin

24 Friday · Aoine

25 Saturday · Satharn

26 Sunday · Domhnach

Rembrandt van Rijn, *Interior with Figures,* **c.1628**

Rembrandt painted this intriguing scene in Leiden before moving to Amsterdam. It depicts a seventeenth-century game known variously as 'la main chaude', 'hot cockles' and 'handjeklap'. It involves one player turning his back to the others and, with eyes shut, holding one hand behind his back. Another player slaps him and the victim has to guess who administered the slap. In this scene, the victim cheats by turning around to spy on his assailant. Others watch, smoke, drink and play music. One figure, in the left foreground, appears as an abstract shape, silhouetted against the light.

M	T	W	T	F	S	S
30	31	1	2	3	4	5
6	7	8	9	10	11	12
13	14	15	16	17	18	19
20	21	22	23	24	25	26
27	28	29	30	1	2	3

27 Monday · Luan

28 Tuesday · Máirt

29 Wednesday · Céadaoin

30 Thursday · Déardaoin

1 Friday · Aoine

December · Nollaig

2 Saturday · Satharn

3 Sunday · Domhnach

David Teniers II, after Titian, *Portrait of a Man,* **1651–1656**

This is a copy of a lost sixteenth-century portrait attributed to Titian, formerly in the collection of Archduke Leopold Wilhelm in Brussels. It is one of several copies by Teniers of Italian paintings from the collection of the Archduke, who was regent of the southern Netherlands from 1647 to 1656. As his court painter, Teniers was in charge of Leopold Wilhelm's art collection, one of the largest and most impressive at the time, and made copies of the most important paintings, showing a fine ability to imitate the style and technique of the Venetian masters.

M	T	W	T	F	S	S
30	31	1	2	3	4	5
6	7	8	9	10	11	12
13	14	15	16	17	18	19
20	21	22	23	24	25	26
27	28	29	30	1	2	3

4 Monday · Luan

5 Tuesday · Máirt

6 Wednesday · Céadaoin

7 Thursday · Déardaoin

8 Friday · Aoine

9 Saturday · Satharn

10 Sunday · Domhnach

Jan Brueghel the Younger & Peter Paul Rubens, *Christ in the House of Martha and Mary,* **c.1628**
Christ, attired in crimson a robe, sits between Martha and Mary of Bethany, the two sisters of Lazarus. Martha's concern with active, material life is implied by her rolled up sleeves, dishevelled apron and working clothes. Mary's association with contemplative, spiritual life is symbolised by her seated pose and sumptuous blue and yellow robes. This picture was a collaboration between two artists: the figures and their flamboyant draperies were painted fluidly by Rubens, while the landscape, animals, birds, fruit and flowers were painted in greater detail by Brueghel the Younger.

M	T	W	T	F	S	S
27	28	29	30	1	2	3
4	5	6	7	8	9	10
11	12	13	14	15	16	17
18	19	20	21	22	23	24
25	26	27	28	29	30	31

11 Monday · Luan

12 Tuesday · Máirt

13 Wednesday · Céadaoin

14 Thursday · Déardaoin

15 Friday · Aoine

16 Saturday · Satharn

17 Sunday · Domhnach

Ernest Meissonier, *A Man Reading Seated at a Table, or The Bibliophile,* **1862**

In his detailed portrayal of dilettanti, Meissonier was influenced by paintings of Dutch seventeenth-century interiors and by eighteenth-century costume and furniture. In this meticulously painted library, a scholar reflects on his writing, dressed in a fan-pleated house coat of silk brocade and seated on a gilded, upholstered armchair. He works at a carved mahogany table with elegant bow legs before an open window, through which daylight shines, illuminating his desk. Numerous bound volumes line the bookshelves, against which lean several folios containing prints or drawings

M	T	W	T	F	S	S
27	28	29	30	1	2	3
4	5	6	7	8	9	10
11	12	13	14	15	16	17
18	19	20	21	22	23	24
25	26	27	28	29	30	31

December · Nollaig
Week 51 · Seachtain 51

18 Monday · Luan

19 Tuesday · Máirt

20 Wednesday · Céadaoin

21 Thursday · Déardaoin

22 Friday · Aoine

23 Saturday · Satharn

24 Sunday · Domhnach
Christmas Eve

Hans Hoffmann, *Hare,* **mid-16th century**

Hans Hoffmann was the most important copyist of the German Renaissance artist Albrecht Dürer. Hoffmann became court painter to Rudolph II in Prague and in 1585 he was paid 200 florins by Rudolph for an oil painting of a hare. He imitated Dürer's charmingly naturalistic, highly detailed watercolour drawing of a hare on more than one occasion: there are copies in Berlin, Dresden, Paris, Rome and Weimar as well as in Dublin. Dürer's celebrated original is signed and dated 1502 and is in the Albertina Museum, Vienna.

M	T	W	T	F	S	S
27	28	29	30	1	2	3
4	5	6	7	8	9	10
11	12	13	14	15	16	17
18	19	20	21	22	23	24
25	26	27	28	29	30	31

December · Nollaig
Week 52 · Seachtain 52

25 Monday · Luan
Christmas Day

26 Tuesday · Máirt
St Stephen's Day

27 Wednesday · Céadaoin

28 Thursday · Déardaoin

29 Friday · Aoine

30 Saturday · Satharn

31 Sunday · Domhnach
New Year's Eve

Bartolomé Esteban Murillo, *The Holy Family,* **mid-17th century**
In this tender scene, Joseph holds the Christ Child and prepares to hand Him to Mary. The Holy Family are portrayed as humble working people, with the tools of Joseph's trade as a carpenter shown in the background. The basket on Mary's knee and the cat curled up beside her complete the domestic atmosphere. Joseph acquired a new prominence in sixteenth-century Spain, no longer being relegated to the background of paintings. Devotion to him grew and an image of a young, paternal Joseph was adopted by Murillo in several versions of the Holy Family.

M	T	W	T	F	S	S
27	28	29	30	1	2	3
4	5	6	7	8	9	10
11	12	13	14	15	16	17
18	19	20	21	22	23	24
25	26	27	28	29	30	31

List of Works